Stella the Spider

written by **Kelly Gaffney**

illustrated by Daniela Dogliani

Stella the Spider hurried across the grass.
"The wind is so strong.
It's time to find a place to hide,"
she said.

"Safe at last," she said,
as she crept under an old pot.

Stella looked back at what was left
of her web.
The wind had knocked over a bike.
It had fallen onto her beautiful web.

"It's time to find a new home,"
said Stella sadly.

Stella peeked out from under the pot.
She looked around the garden.
Over by a big tree was a kennel.
"That looks like a good place
to spin my new web," she said.

Stella hurried across the garden
and went up the side
of the kennel.
Slowly she began to spin her web.

All of a sudden, an enormous dog
ran out of the kennel.
"Maybe this is **not** such a good place
for a web," cried Stella.

Stella dropped to the ground
and hurried towards the house.
She ran up a post and began
to make her web.

The web was almost finished
when the door opened,
and out rushed a little girl.

6

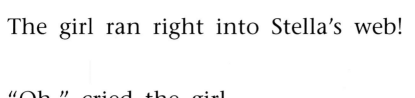

The girl ran right into Stella's web!

"Oh," cried the girl.
"A spider's web!"

8

Poor Stella!

She ran under the steps
and hid from the little girl.
"This house is **not** a good place
for my web," she said sadly.

Stella felt tired.
Maybe she would never find
a new home.

Stella looked around the garden.
She wondered where else she could
make her web.

Stella looked at the big tree.
It was beside the kennel.
Maybe the tree would be
a good place for her web.

Stella made her way carefully
across the garden.
She didn't want to be stepped on
by a big dog or a little girl!
Stella took her time, creeping under
the bushes and the long grass.

At last she came to the big tree.
She looked up into its enormous branches.
Little bugs were flying around the leaves.
"This looks like a good place for a web,"
smiled Stella.

She crept up the trunk of the tree.
It was cool and dark.
Stella went out on a branch
and hid under a big green leaf.

Looking down at the garden, Stella felt safe. Slowly she crept out from under the leaf. She began to spin a web between the branches.

"Here is my new home," Stella said happily.